WHAT MAY HAVE BEEN

Letters of Jackson Pollock & Dori G

A Novel

Susan Tepper and Gary Percesepe

Červená Barva Press
Somerville, Massachusetts

BOOKS BY THE AUTHORS

Susan Tepper

Blue Edge. Červená Barva Press, 2006

Deer & Other Stories. Wilderness House Press, 2009

Gary Percesepe

Free Spirits: Feminist Philosophers on Culture.
With Kate Mehuron. Prentice Hall, 1995

Ethics: Personal and Social Responsibility in a Diverse World.
Prentice Hall, 1995

Philosophy: An Introduction to the Labor of Reason.
Macmillan, 1990

Future(s) of Philosophy: The Marginal Thinking of Jacques Derrida.
Peter Lang Publishing Co., 1989

WHAT MAY HAVE BEEN

Letters of Jackson Pollock & Dori G

A Novel

—the kiss will be brackish
making a dam, then another and my lips
against the sky backing up...

Simon Perchik, *Rafts*

What May Have Been: Letters of Jackson Pollock and Dori G is a work of fiction in the form of letters exchanged between the artist Jackson Pollock and the fictional character Dori G. The events, opinions and discussions contained in the characters' letters are the authors' invention and should not be construed as factual.

Červená Barva Press
P.O. Box 440357
W. Somerville, MA 02144-3222

www.cervenabarvapress.com

http://www.thelostbookshelf.com/WhatMayHaveBeen.html

Cover and Book Design by William J. Kelle

Cover Photograph Copyright © Gary Percesepe

ISBN: 978-0-9844732-8-1

Library of Congress Control Number: 2010931817

AUTHORS' NOTE

Jackson Pollock may or may not have written letters to, and
/or received letters from, one or more women who figured in
his life. However, all of the letters contained in this book,
and the prologue and epilogue, are entirely fictional and
should be read as such. For factual information about
Jackson Pollock or Lee Krasner, the reader should consult
biographical or other non-fictional sources pertaining to
them.

The letters of Jackson Pollock were written by Susan Tepper,
and the letters of Dori G by Gary Percesepe.

Susan Tepper and Gary Percesepe had never met when they
decided to write a book together. They knew each other's
work from Fictionaut, a social networking site for writers that
features some of the best new writing on the web. They
began exchanging emails about writing and editing, and
discovered that Susan lived in New Jersey, while Gary was a
native New Yorker who once had an almost girlfriend who
lived in a town near the one that Susan named. Susan once
owned a home in The Springs, not far from Montauk, where
Gary often vacationed. The Springs had been the home of
the painter Jackson Pollock. Both Susan and Gary knew the
roadhouse where he had his last drink before his fatal car
crash, and had drinks there (on separate occasions). From
these serendipitous emails came an idea: why not write a
book together about Jackson and a young girl. Shouldn't the
form of the book be letters, since it was their emails that had
occasioned the writing? They agreed to this arrangement,
with one condition: they would not meet in person or even
talk on the phone until after the book was complete. The
result, dear reader, you hold in your hands.
When the book was complete, Gary and Susan met for drinks
at Pastis, in Greenwich Village. They are still friends.

Pollock held the car to fifty. As he drove east from the city his optimism vanished. The color of the day was drained from the sky. He picked up Route 27. The land began to change. In the air was the faint smell of the sea. He passed the burnt out foundation of an ancient house set back from the road. Here and there along the road isolated frame houses held nothing of what he wanted. It was almost night when he passed through Amagansett. He turned off on Old Montauk Highway.

She was waiting by the dune.

Dori,

I been feeling itchy all day. It could be the green flies, I don't
know, but my arms are bleeding that's how much I
scratched. When you see me again you'll think a rat ate my
arms. Dori, you scared of rats? You don't seem the type to
scare but then maybe you do. Maybe you just do. Lee
doesn't scare. She can make a lot of noise, a mouse runs
through the kitchen she screams and jumps on a chair. I
think it's all pretend. She can smell you around me, she's got
a sixth sense like an animal. There is no scaring that woman.
I can smell you around me. I smell you when I work. You're
in the blue enamel I thin inside the coffee can, I smell you
when I drip aluminum paint. Probably you have no idea what
I'm talking about right? You think all paint smells the same.
Shitty. Well it don't. I have paint that smells like eyes, and
some like burnt skin. Guess what yours smells like? Don't
be scared, OK?
Jackson

Darling, this will be short. I snatched your letter out of Mother's hands— she's been impossible. I love her madly but I can't talk to her. I don't think she knows but you'd better send to the post office box number I gave you. Why didn't you? From now on— please!!

I don't understand your painting. I don't want to. I don't want to be your paint, or your painting. I want you. But I don't WANT to want you.

Only eight days till school is out here. I count the hours. Father says he has a job lined up for me this summer. He won't tolerate whining. All my girlfriends are jealous. They see me skipping along and they wonder. Don't worry. They know I am crazy. Everyone does.

All my life I've been impersonating a normal person. Like I've been in training for you—
I am lonesome without you. Please come again soon. You are like a big white cat, wise behind the whiskers, but you don't look like your pictures. I saw that picture in the Times and I laughed. You hide so well.

Please don't talk about your wife. That scares me. I don't want to know anything darling, my head is empty. I have ideas but no one to share them with. I wish someone were in love with me, like when I was little and the boys would all chase me. I scare them now. I sit with my pretty empty blonde head not noticing them and they've learned to leave me alone.

Come!

D

Dori, What job? What do you need a job for? You're too young to work, your mother should be spanked! You need to play on the beach, get tan. Come to think of it, I've never seen you with a tan. Your skin is pure. It's the purity of you. You're like a little girl playing big. Why do you keep calling me darling? It's silly Dori. You don't need to pretend like those Park Avenue socialites. They come to look at my pictures and stand there hemming and hawing, they don't know what to make of them. You have your womanly things in place Dori. Keep the whiteness of your skin. What's your mother look like? Is she gorgeous like you? Maybe I'll be meeting her sometime, what do you think? Good idea? I'm just kidding. I have to go into the city again for a while. Not sure how long. Here's what. Tie a little string on my horse post over near the silver maple so I'll see it when I drive up. A little white string, nothing big or (you know who) might catch wind and take it down. See, I respect you Dori. I didn't say the name because you asked me not to. I respect you more than just about any woman I've ever known. Don't be alarmed by small things like paint and wives. It's all very small in the scheme of things. You'll see what I mean one of these days. Let's meet up as soon as I'm back from the city. I really need to fuck you, no kidding. I'll leave a message for you at The Salt Bar, a note so there's no more slip-ups. I'll leave it with Rusty the bartender with the plaid suspenders. He knows how to stay mum. I can't keep that postal box number in my head, it flies away like geese. It's still cold at night and I want to feel you.
Jackson

jackson,

it feels funny to call you that so i make it small letters. if i
write small enough i can fit it all on the back of this picture.
my so called senior picture. do i look senior to you? do you
really want to fuck this senior?

my mom is tall and blonde like me. i have her looks.
everyone says so. i have heard it said that she does not have a
kind face, it's more a classical beauty, one misplaced chisel
stroke from being cruel around the mouth. a terrible beauty.
if you saw her you would want her, too. she is more your
age. you are old! i know you hate when i say that but you are
old old old!

i am amazed to be this old. when i was little i had many
problems. i wasn't developing normally. they made me see
some stupid doctors who said i had mental trouble. i was
sent to mclean where they tried to break me, outside boston,
but it didn't work.

you see the smile here? it's for you. if i was dust I would
gather on the floor below your bed and sleep beneath you till
you swept me up. i kiss you— d

Dori,

I'm sorry everything went wrong. She saw the string you tied
in a bow and she took it down. She didn't say so but when I
drove up it wasn't there, then she saw me outside looking on
the ground and later that night she said I found your
girlfriend's bow. That's how I knew you'd tied a bow.
Sweet! It went right to my heart, Dori, that little bow. Now
let's get a few things straight here. Why do you have a
problem with my name? It's a simple name, not like a foreign
name that's hard to pronounce. Just say Jackson when we
meet and it will be solved. Press against me hard, say
Jackson. Trust me on this. And I want to have that picture.
You hear? Give it to me on Wednesday. I thought I'd see
you by now but she's got me stalked, I can't take a piss with
the door closed. Listen Dori, I don't want you to sleep on
the floor like dust. People do bad things. Your parents
probably thought they were helping you but christ! People
like them should be shot. I know that kind of help. No help
help. Your mother is nothing to me, I don't care what she
fucking looks like. And don't you believe the bad things you
hear. I did not take a piss in anyone's fireplace despite what
the newspapers said. And of course I want to fuck you, god,
I live to fuck you. It's painting and fucking you. That's all.
(not necessarily in that order).
Jackson

where are you? you don't write anymore. i put the string out, i talk to rusty every day, he says you can't leave the city. what am i supposed to think of that. i hate you for leaving me here. i hate my stupid job. i work at this stupid candy store in bridgehampton selling candy to the idiot children of the rich, and worse, their phony parents. i want to die. where are you?

you say you want to fuck me. then you do fuck me, and then it is enough? i am your fix? i cannot fix you. i cannot fix me.

when i was little i wanted to be a writer for a while, then a painter, but what i really wanted was to join the circus. dori the high wire girl! i wanted the crowds at the circus to see me and weep. to work together to hope i didn't fall. there is always somewhere to fall from, don't you think so?

forget the string, forget rusty. get over here before i go crazy.

your dori

Dori you sound in a panic. I wrote to you, I swear it. I told you about the bow, how Lee took it down, I told you everything. What's going on here? Where did that letter go? I'm back, Dori honey, I'm back and I'm eager to see you.
Yours,
Jackson

Dear Mr. Pollock,

Your young slip of a girl— your mistress, sir— was observed breaking and entering the chemistry lab here at Vassar. She was caught with three other girls, red handed— or blue handed. They got the mimeograph ink all over themselves trying to steal the midterm. Mother is distraught. Father is beside himself. She is back in Montauk. Blue, indeed.

She asks: what are you painting? What is that in your hand, right now?

Yours sincerely,

Robert Barkalot
Dean of Students

Dori I know I've been absent from your life. It can't be helped. They mounted a show of my pictures in New York and that took up some time. My family came for a visit, the whole Pollock clan. A lot of things get in the way, Dori. I can't expect you to understand because you're young. You are so young it hurts me in the belly. You called me old. It made me laugh. I am so fucking old I feel like I could drop dead bent over the canvas. My knees are giving out. Did I tell you I've given up the drink? Now what are you doing in Montauk? You run off to Vassar, now it's Montauk. I think you should come home. Springs misses you, the pond misses you, the ducks were calling your name the other night! Even The General Store misses you (well your money). But I miss you Dori. It's more than just drink and fucking. Screw Vassar. It's time to be my girl again.
Always,
Jackson

PS— get this — some crazy professor wrote me a letter about you. Dear Mr. Pollock it said. I laughed my ass off. Did you get arrested? I hope you told that stuffed shirt to stick it where the sun don't shine.

PPS— I like that scarf you tie around your hair, the one with the swirling colors. Don't ever dye your hair that ugly platinum. Why do some people find it attractive on women? You have hair the color of young corn (there's a paint that shade but I won't mention it or you will get upset with me). But aren't you getting used to me being a painter? A little?

I'm down, Dori, way way down this morning. You know about these fall nights here, the cold gets in deep and I stretched canvas until long past midnight. I could hear the owls so maybe it was around five when I finished. I found a red canvas I thought was lost for good. It pulled me up for about a minute or two. My studio I'm happy to have, don't get me wrong, it's a godsend that studio but the cold got into me like a death— I can't explain. She had people here all weekend, my friends, but I couldn't get into it. Everybody drinking and dancing and carousing and finally I went out back and worked. Rollo (my painter friend) wanted to help but I sent him away. She says sooner or later I send people away. My hands were so stiff and I needed you to touch to get my blood flowing back through my fingers.
Jackson

Dori meet me Tuesday at Rusty's ex-wife's house in the dunes. She's on a freighter going around the world and the place is empty. He said it was OK for me to use as long as I don't leave trash around. I gotta get out of here a while or I'll decompose. You-know-who has been sitting on the stool in the corner watching me work. Every day for a week she's been there still as a statue. It's a deliberate tactic. Anyway, you know the house, we biked there last summer— it's got a red door and a rooster statue out front. We did it in the hammock and I fell out. I thought I broke my back, I yelped like a hound. Remember? You couldn't stop laughing. It's only a couple miles outside of town. Go on your bike and I'll drive you back in the Ford. Go there and wait for me, OK? Wear your scarf with the swirls. Don't wear underpants. Your legs are like white asparagus stalks, I want them squeezing my neck tight.

Dori I went to Rusty's ex-wife's place and waited for you. I thought maybe you forgot which house so I walked the streets then drove through the dunes looking for you. It is desolate there after the summer. You know I can't take this shit. I need to phone you, this is fucking prehistoric— why don't we use a carrier pigeon to send notes like in the war? Why didn't you come? I waited a long time. I stood there looking at the bed and I pictured you there on the white sheet. I could paint you in that house. Why won't you let me? I could paint you sweet and innocent like I did that socialite portrait in the magazine. Or how about this— I make your face invisible behind a veil. Nobody will know. I'll paint you from the neck down. Nobody can figure out my pictures anyway so they'll never figure out it's you. Dori I can't sleep nights. I work all night then try to sleep a little during the day. Are you sick or something? Is it those parents? I gotta see you or else.
Jackson

Jesus. Jesus jesus jesus. Something went wrong I can feel it. Dori I know you're out there. Is it because I can't say love?

You got me drinking. That's right little girl. I hope you're proud of yourself. Drinking and painting, that's my whole life now.

Lee is gonna kick my ass to mars. She hid the bottles in the wood pile. Stupid place to hide a man's liquor. We had some fight over it. She broke a few which is real dumb. Nothing dumber than wasting good booze. You could come here, you know. I've had girls over. That's before I met you. Not since, Dori honey, not since. I hope you believe that. She minds but won't open a mouth to me. Afraid I will leave her FOR GOOD. Come around back to my studio, OK? It's the old barn on the property. It was blocking Accabonac Creek so I had it moved. You should've seen that! I thought it would slide right off the flat truck all busted to pieces. Dori come bare assed and ready. I want to show you a special picture, it's called *The Tea Cup*. I look at it and think of you. You'd like it, there's a heart practically dead center. Even if the rest makes no sense, you can't miss the crooked heart. You have to accept my life sooner or later.
Yours,
Jackson

J,

I'm in Montauk hiding out. After I got kicked out of school I couldn't bear facing my parents. I'm staying with a friend. I don't dare tell you where. I know what you'll do. I need to be alone right now. I don't know what I'm doing with my life. I can't bear to see you, or anyone right now, only this pounding surf. I watch the white lines approaching the shore thinking each wave is a message, but none comes. The only comfort I have is the long line of waves, crashing. They are relentless. The ocean doesn't care about us or our problems. Somehow that is a comfort to me.

Seeing you seems more painful than not seeing you. I have to figure this out for myself.

d

OK then. I wrote you a note and ripped it up. Stay there. Don't write me no more. You act like a little girl you get no candy. The waves mean nothing to me. Nothing.

Are you kidding? What do I see in you? Ask that question ten years from now. I can always buy more liquor. Meantime Dori don't write me anymore.

Dori, I don't need two bitches. You cut a hole in me then you look at the waves?

You are impossible.

I like that.

d

You make spider webs in my head and that's no good. I'm going to break from you if you keep hiding. You're not the only girl out there. Girls are all over the place. You should see what it's like in the city. More beauty than one universe can hold. Get over it Dori. Whatever is eating you, get over it. Come back, I'll show you *Water Birds*. I did that one long before I knew you. My water bird loves the waves. Fly back little Dori.

This girl is not all over the place. She's right here.

Meet me tomorrow at the Montauk lighthouse, 6 pm. I'll be the one standing at the point without panties.

It's my birthday. Maybe you'll get lucky.

Just whistle for me. You do know how to whistle don't you?

d

Oh, boy. Well you have learned a thing or two in college. Just whistle for you. Boy it made me laugh. So you think you're a movie star? I suppose you're smoking Camels now and drinking bourbon. Listen, I've been thinking about what you said about me wanting your body. It's true, I want your body. I don't need a woman's mind. You have to know that about me. Lee has a mind and I want to cook it on the barbecue pit. A mind is attached to a voice and I've got enough of that all the time. I run out of the house to get away from that and she follows me. I only want your voice when you're under me and whimpering for more. I want you to call me Jackson. I want to hear it so bad I felt it in the brush like it was my arm all chewed up by you.

Jackson, Jackson, say it baby and I'll come running like a dog. You won't need to whistle. I'll be there at 6. How old are you now?

What you don't know about women is a lot.

Don't be late.

I'm 18 you horny bastard.

Leave your paint home. I'm the picture.

d

I want you to come live with me Dori. You're of age
now. Do you like the locket? I made sure to get the chain
long enough for you to hide it down inside your blouse. I
can't explain what it was like being alone.
I got so fucking empty. Like all my blood emptied into the
toilet instead of piss. Right now I can smell your hair and
your legs. Hey, wait until you hear this. I go into the market
today and there you are! I got so happy! I mean for a minute
I thought this girl was you. I called out your name and she
didn't turn around so I followed her down the aisle and then
it wasn't you. And I felt like a bomb went off in my head. I
got dizzy a minute. The bread was moving on the shelf like it
was flying past me, all these loaves shooting by. Worse than
coming off any drunk. So you should come live with me.
We can live in my house. I'll send Lee back to the city. I
need you with me all the time, I can see that now. I have
these holes, Dori, huge holes I can't fill by myself. See that's
why I paint. And drink. It's paint and drink or I die. But
you could help me there. Just being around, seeing you so
young and perfect every day. Pure. I would drink your
menstrual blood. Don't be alarmed by that. It's just how
deep I feel for you.
Always,
Jackson

I'll send you some in a cup.

d

No matter what happens from this point forward Dori, I'm going to tell you a few things. You can take it or leave it. It felt like you threw a pail of shit in my face. That's right. I go to you at your command and I love you all night. That's right. I loved you all night. Now with your wise ass college girl mind you probably are thinking he means he fucked me all night. I did fuck you. But Dori you were there and you know it was more than that. I slept with my head in your muff half the night, I was like your slave. Do you know how long since I bought a woman a piece of jewelry? That little heart locket is my heart to yours. I didn't have time to get it engraved, they have to send it out to do that. You only gave me ONE DAY NOTICE! Your eighteenth birthday and one day notice? Were you thinking about letting it just go by without me? Christ! But with your new college girl mentality I bet you're laughing. Dori go ahead and laugh at me. But I'll also tell you this. That blood thing you wrote, well I started to see it different. I saw the gold chalice the priest lifts up to heaven, and it was filled with your menstrual blood. All day when I painted it was your blood I dripped on the canvas.

I love the locket you gave me. I am twirling it on its thin gold chain right now.

I had two months of so called college before they threw me out. It's not as though they made me head of the psychology department. You are so dramatic! You make everything sound like a crisis going off. When I am not near you I feel your absence, your absence fills the room, but when you are present your intensity scares me. I feel like Friday on the lost island with Robinson Crusoe. You came at me like a maniac. When there are only two people on the island and one of them is mad it is a scary thing.

You are a drug. When I take you I feel better but it cannot stop the craving for more. But when I stay off you the craving drives me crazy. So whether you are here or whether you are absent you haunt me. You're both the poison and the cure.

If I ever left you I wouldn't have the strength to just stop seeing you. I'd just disappear.

I love to watch you sleep. It's the only time I really see your face settle into something like peace. I brushed your hair and stroked your neck and felt the blood vessels beneath my fingers, throbbing. It's not my blood you're after, it's my soul. You're a soul vampire. How many girls have you seduced with that look— when you first looked at me, that day at the fruit market in Amagansett, I felt like you wanted to eat me up. That look set me on fire, and I've been burning since. My life is a fire, but little else.

I don't know what to do with you, but I don't know what to do without you.

I'm cooked. D

Say my name dammit! Say it! Say it! JACKSON. And stop making believe about everything. You need to come live with me.

You say come and live with me. But you don't know what you are saying. Did you even read what I wrote? What are you going to do about her? Where would I live? What kind of life would it be?

You're like the sun AND the moon. You're in orbit around yourself. You can barely take care of yourself, how would you take care of me?

I went to the market today and a boy was there, checking me out at the register. He couldn't stop looking at me. He had puppy dog eyes, he looked like a bloodhound. I think he is the son of one of the local fishermen in town. He couldn't even bring himself to speak to me. When I left I looked back and he melted into a puddle.

Jackson, Jackson, Jackson. You're mad.

dori

You did it, you said my name. Can you feel me smiling?
Always,
Jackson

Dori I read your last letter over again. It was in my pocket
and I reached in to get a rag to wipe off my hands and got
paint on your letter. Now you're a marked woman! (a joke
Dori). You trying to make me jealous of some wet behind
the ears townie? Be careful or you'll find yourself married to
one and you'll never escape this place. For me this is escape,
but for you it will be prison without parole. Is that the life
you want? Beautiful girls can escape you know. I'm your
ticket out. Meet me at Rusty's ex-wife's house on Friday.
I made an extra key and put it under the picnic bench out
back. See— I think about you all the time. I want you to
meet my friends next time they come in from the city. I want
you to sit on my lap with your hands around my neck and let
everyone know you belong to me.

Jackson

You can't make me jealous. Lee wants a baby.

So give her one. What are you waiting for?

Beautiful girls cannot escape themselves.

And what is beauty, anyway? Who gets to decide? Are your paintings considered beautiful? I don't think they are. I don't think I am. My legs are too long. My hips are narrow like a boy's. My nose is too small. My eyes are set far apart so I feel like a cow.

Have I escaped from you? Has my beauty helped me to do that?

Sure, I'll come. It will be swell. I can't have you jealous. Hold that ticket.

d

That was low down. I didn't expect that from you. It
is what's known as a DOMESTIC PROBLEM.
Not livestock— but a wife who wants a baby for
protection. You're too young to understand. I won't hold it
against you, what you said. Nothing between us is changed.
OK? Right?

You make it complicated Dori. I can't think now, I have to go out back and work more. It's so damn cold and the wind comes through spaces in the barn boards, I feel it on my back when I bend over to work. There's no light, I had to string a lantern. I had a bad supper. A stew with too many vegetables. I got upset. Meat is what I need to keep warm I told her. Look, Dori, lousy things are said about me every day! The art world is a shark pool. And here you go worrying about beauty that is a given. Get a mirror for chrissakes! Maybe you're fishing compliments from me? You have to curb your insecurity, it will make you sick. Look— some say my work is a fake. I read it in the papers and laugh myself silly. How can you fake a picture? Unless you're copying one that's already been done.

Certain things cannot be faked. Keep that under your silky scarf with the swirling colors. I think that scarf is invading the painting I'm doing. That means you, Dori— you invading the picture.

Forever,
Jackson

If I ever had a baby I would hope for a boy. I would not know what to do with a baby girl, how I could shield her from what awaits her. To be called pretty pretty pretty and dressed up and petted like a doll. With a boy maybe I could impart something of myself without worrying. If I had a girl I would spend the days crying. But I don't know what I am talking about. Someone would have to explain to me why to bring a baby into this crazy world. Because face it, the world is an awful fucking place. Why does she think a baby will protect her? I don't get that at all. Protect her from what? Why does she feel she needs protection? Is she protecting herself from you? Hard to know how a baby would help with that, as you would just hurt them both. You're a bruiser. What have you done to her, Jackson?

Do you love her? If not, why don't you let go of her? Isn't the best part of love the letting go? Or is that only in the movies. If love means the same as possess count me out, is what I say. I love my parents but I can't go back there. I miss them sometimes, but it's not a disaster. I have a job lined up here. I want to make money. I want my own things. I want a room that is mine because I earned it.

Please take care of yourself, Jackson. I worry about you sometimes. Yes, does that surprise you? Well, it's true. I know you think I don't care about you, or that I don't care about you enough, or care every day, or that I only care about what is in front of me, but that's not true. But I have to do what I think is best. Right now that means seeing you. But one day it might not. I really think sometimes that I am older than you. Or maybe girls are just more practical, because we have to be. We only get one chance. And like you said, it's my body. It's the only one I have. So please talk to her about babies. I don't mean to be cruel, but please remember that I am a single girl without money living in a room that is borrowed, and you are not. You are a famous artist. Our situations are not exactly the same. your dori

Little Dori,

You are almost silly. But I don't like to hear you use the word fuck when you write me a letter. Only say fuck when you want me to fuck you. Otherwise, Dori, you're talking tramp talk. And that's no good for a beautiful girl of eighteen. You talk like that people get the wrong idea. Men. Bad men will come knocking at your door. Now let me tell you a few things. A wife gets worried about keeping her man so she schemes and gets herself knocked up. That traps most men to staying. I would lose her in a minute but Lee is an octopus. She's got all these arms and legs and schemes. Just when I think I've pushed her as far as she'll take it, she comes up with some new plan to make my life better. Vegetables, hiding my booze, having my friends down on weekends. It never makes me better. But she believes it does and that's all that matters to her. People believe something you can't pry it loose with a wrench. I never hit her, you shouldn't think those things! Why do you call me a bruiser? It sounds like you saw a movie with your girlfriends. What did you see— Bogart? He's a little tough guy. Oh, sweet Dori. I guess I'm somewhat known but I'm not rich. You want a rich painter then go to Spain and live with Picasso. You don't understand about art. I might get rich some day but who knows? They need to sponsor you and pay big money for the pictures, get a lot into the museums. I want you back in Springs. Get back here! Get a room nearby so I can see you every day. Montauk is too far. I'm taking you with me to the city next time. Hell. I want you on my arm. Forever.
Jackson

Jackson,

I will go to the city with you. But I want you to do something for me. Listen to me, ok? I want to go back to school. I want you to help me get into NYU and I want you to pay for it. I can't ask my parents.

Listen! You can see me down there. We can live freely in the Village. You say you want me. So please, do this for me.

I want this. I need to develop my mind and come up with a plan. School is it. There is so much I want to know. I miss being in the city. Please, Jackson, do this for me! You have friends you can ask to help me, too.

Do I sound like a spoiled child? I'm sorry. But I want this. This is something you can do for me. I'll pay you back, every penny, I swear. I'll find a way. I can waitress, and I want to act. You and your pals can help me.

This morning I followed a squirrel. He didn't know where he was going either. He scampered back and forth in front of his tree, stopping to see if I was still watching him. He'd climb ten feet up the tree and stop, then jump to the other side of the tree so I couldn't see him. Then he'd run down the tree and start over. I know how he feels.

d

No, Dori, this is all wrong. I have to be here to work, I can't move back to the city. You didn't understand me right. You come live with me here and we can travel back and forth to the city. Dori I can't send you to college. I'm hardly past the days when I traded paintings for food and beer (you think I'm kidding ask The General Store), they kept me going one winter. Here I have a place to work, a house. We can have a grand life you and me. If you wanted college why did you make a mess at Vassar? That had to cost your Daddy a pretty penny or two. Dori Dori. You live in a dream world. Let me paint your picture. It will relieve some of my stress and I can paint standing straight again. You'll be lying down and I'll be standing over you painting. Do the practical thing. Get the extra key from Rusty's ex's yard and meet me in there on Monday. She ain't gonna be on that fucking freighter forever! It makes my cock hard to think about it (about you). I always need you.
Jackson

All day I hear you crying. Maybe you're not but I hear you just the same. This is no good. I get distracted by a woman's tears. You're so mixed up Dori. You're a squirrel, you're a college girl, you go to Vassar, you go to the city. What do you mean when you say you miss the city? You lived out east your whole life. How can you miss what you don't know. Here is your life in the city: a cold water flat like my dump on East 8th Street, cockroaches in the sink, a leaking bathtub from overhead that the landlord don't fix. Now I'm starting to feel less sad for you and somewhat angry. You don't know how good you have it. You go live in the city and wait tables your looks will fade in five years. Now are you coming on Monday or not?
Jackson

You don't want me to paint another *She-Wolf* picture from all this torture you're laying on me Dori. You don't want me that way.

I went home to mother and father. The mental troubles are back. Oh, Jackson, I feel so broken and humiliated. I am wasting my time pretending the trouble with my head is curable or preventable. I am in a terribly nervous state. Mother gives me warm milk at night and stays in my room holding my hand to help me sleep. She called the doctor in. He said that introspection is not good for a highly nervous state like mine, and then they asked me about boys, and whether something is upsetting me? They called my friend in Montauk to see if she would talk. They're bound to find out about us if they keep asking around and I want to cry and spill my guts for everyone on the floor, so maybe those were my cries you were hearing?

Oh Jackson, I don't know what to do! What will become of us? My father wants to send me back to McLean. They caught me digging at my skin. I don't want you to worry about me, but worry is all I do. I'm so sorry I ruined your life. I am just a child, after all, I am regressing, I don't know what is in my head that makes me like this. I cannot seem to break out of this nervous state. I may have to go away, Jackson. I don't want to. I want to come to you but I can't.

I don't trust myself. I can't look forward or backward. I am stuck and I hate my life.

Save yourself.

d

I'm befuddled, Dori, I don't know what to do. I'm pacing in circles. Rusty gave me your letter last night. I went in for a beer and he says to me a friend of your lass dropped this off. I read it right there standing up at the bar. My hands got shaky. I read it a few times and I thought about swallowing it. I thought if I swallow what she wrote, then shit it out, it will be flushed away forever. Then I didn't. I kept it in my hand because right now it's all I have of you. Now listen to me. You are not crazy! It's those parents keeping you down on some mental level. They want you always as their little girl. Dori you gotta get out of there! I read about the warm milk and the hand holding and I felt nauseated. Hold my cock and you will get better. Hold it tight as you want, you can't hurt me. I'll pour all my cock energy into you and it will bring you up again. You need to come here. Lee is going away on Tuesday for a week. Come then. If you don't you'll never get away from them. Dori, I'm begging you.

jackson,

you always wanted me to say your name.

i've failed everybody i love.

they're sending me away again. i will have to write to you in
lipstick, no sharp objects allowed in there—

i wanted to be the one to show you things you'd never seen
before
i wanted you to show me places I've never seen. there are so
many
loving you was like learning another language
you know how I feel, I hate when you doubt it

you're the only one that ever gets me, the only one to
take me.
am i saying this in a way you can understand?

dori

Come here Tuesday! You can do it! Walk out Dori and be
with me. I know you'll come and I'll be waiting.
Forever.
Jackson

Before you, all I could see was a pit. Dori look what you've
done for me already! I'm partly to blame for your troubles.
I'll never call you a little girl again. Inside your body I reach
the center of the earth.

Tuesday! Tuesday! Don't lose track of time.

You were like a half-grown deer coming into my studio. You stood there in the doorway looking so curious but also afraid, delicate. I felt like I'd been far away for a long time. I got this rush of air in my ears. Dori you're thinner but it hasn't affected your beauty. I'm sorry if I rushed at you. It was like I'd been stuffed full of firecrackers about to go off, I saw that it startled you but then you melted. Thank god because for a minute or two I got scared you'd run away. Do you know it's the first time I ever carried a woman in my arms. When I carried you through the grass on into the house I knew you as my true bride. When I placed you on the bed and said those things, you didn't have to cry. You aren't used to things being good so when a good thing happens you get turned inside out. I understand that. I used to be like that with my work. Finally some good thing would happen after so much bad, and what did I do? I got drunk. Not to feel happy but to get away from the goodness of it. It's like you're living in the rain for so long and then the sun shines and you run to close the shades, you're afraid to go outside like the sun might burn right through you. Dori you have skin like rice paper. Some time when we go to the city I'll take you to the museum to see the Japanese paintings on rice paper. They are very fine. So are you, Dori. Now when I die at least I'll have something good to carry into the next life. I never had a week this good. I believe you were happy too. You seemed happy. We need to make a plan. Meanwhile I want you to stay put in the cabin. Your parents will never think to look for you there. It's a sweet little place, isn't it? It's nice having the bay out the back door. The owners won't be home from Europe until June so there's plenty of time. Once we got the fireplace going and the cobwebs brushed aside, it was real nice and homey. I can come and see you every day. Do you think you can be happy there a while, Dori?
PS— I'm sorry you got paint on your shoes. I'll buy you new ones, ten pair if you like.
Forever and a day, Jackson
PPS— Your hair looks good cut this new shorter way.

My shoes, ha! They look like one of your canvases now. I stuck some wildflowers in them and put them on a small table by the door and I look at them all day. I go around barefoot in the cabin, or sit outside staring at the bay. My feet are dirty and I need a bath but I don't care. I can stay here, Jackson? You are sure? They won't come for me here? I hear noises sometimes and I startle easily. I'm no good at being alone, though I'd like to be. Everything seems different to me. The world has turned. I feel grown up and then I get scared again. My emotions change every 30 seconds. When are you coming? How long can you stay?

Stay dirty till I get there. I want to fuck you dirty. Then we'll take a bath. When it's warm again I'll bathe you in the bay. I got this big natural sea sponge some Greek was selling on a street corner in the city.

Spongie he called out as you walked by. It cost me a quarter for this great big sponge. I'll be there soon, Dori, promise.
Jackson

I want you to dress me and bathe me and wash my hair and dry it. Then brush it one hundred strokes. I want you to take care of me, Jackson.

You've worn me down and made me love you. There. I said it. Now what do we do?

Come!

I will I will I will I will. Promise.

Well Dori, was it worth the wait? You were so cute in the little kitchen, reminded me of a little home-maker doll the way you flipped those hotcakes so perfect. The best hotcakes I ever ate in my life. See, you can do anything you put your mind to. Bet I could teach you to paint. Would you like that? I could start by teaching you how to mix color. In most cases never start with the white. You go the other way, white comes later. I learned that as a rule in the beginning but you know what I think of rules. Anyway, I believe you'd like watercolor, my little sea bird. The way the paint slips and slides on the paper, kind of how you like to watch the waves roll in and out. I could teach you to paint watercolor. You could take an easel and sit by the ocean and paint all day. You will never know such peace Dori. I think the realist painters are the most peaceful, they take what's there in front of them and make it more perfect. It's the rest of us who have to fool around with form that get in trouble down the line. Some critic called one of my pictures the devil's work. Can you believe it! What kind of nut comes up with shit like that? Anyway it started a big brouhaha among some religious sects. I didn't even know about it at the time. That kind of crap goes right past me. But my sponsor then, she said it made good publicity! Bad words made good publicity! Amazing, right? Dori you looked like an angel when you slept. I saw the calm move into your face the moment I made you come. That's when I knew everything would be all right again.

Did you always want to paint? I cannot remember everything
I wanted when I was little. But I always wanted to act.
Mother made it clear that this was unacceptable but I wanted
it anyway. I loved the idea of being giant sized up on the
screen, preserved forever in that peculiar light— light
perpetual. I saw myself kissing a handsome man, up on the
tall screen, or me running to the water (I always loved the
water), or walking through a sea of sunflowers— I wanted to
see and be seen. I wanted to be loved and wanted by millions
of people I didn't know. Is this how it feels for you when
someone tells you they were moved by one of you paintings?

But I couldn't bear the idea of a critic. How do you criticize
what is in a person's heart, that they express, their art? I
don't understand that. It's like their private vision of the
world, so how can someone say, well no, I'm sorry, that
vision is wrong. How can it be wrong when you see it? I
don't understand right or wrong when it comes to art, but I
guess someone could say I don't understand morals at all, I
am an unmarried woman sleeping with an older man while he
lives with another woman. It is all very confusing to me, but
it is best not to think about it. But I do.

I like when you call me a seabird. I have always loved the
water. As a little girl I played for hours in the ocean, standing
my little body up to the surf. When we were at the beach I
never wanted to go home.

Now I am home, but where am I really? Is this home now?
Nothing seems to last.

I like when you shush me and make love to me. You have a
kiss for every worry. I know I keep you busy. I am a full
time girl, aren't I?

your dori

Dori, Dori. You are my full time girl. Who'd want you any other way? You have so many thoughts and questions. But that's good. Well let's see now. You say I don't read your letters or answer your questions. I read every word! Did I always want to be a painter? I don't know. My brothers were painters before me. I was the baby of the family. Twice I got kicked out of high school in Los Angeles. I didn't learn the first time, I had to go and do it twice. I guess I was what they call a punk kid. For a while I named myself Hugo and went to communist meetings. I don't think those things turned me into a painter. Maybe it was my study of the mystics. I don't really know. My work's been called mystical whatever the hell that's supposed to mean. I don't think you'd like being an actress Dori. It's way more than what you see, what you see is the finished product. It's a lot of long hours under hot lights. You're beautiful enough, for sure, but is it right for you? Those actresses who seem nice and wholesome are tough old birds— not like my sweet sea bird. Did you know most of them are whores? That's right, Dori. They fuck to get the part. Could you do that? Could you fuck some fat slob producer to get the part? I don't think you could. Dori I don't think you can fuck without some love attached. There's no love out in Hollywood land. I've met some of those people in the city and they can be very tricky. Nice to your face and ice down your back. It ain't a good way to live. I don't recommend it. I'm reading your letter once more. Don't want to forget to answer any questions, then you'll get mad at me and shut me out. You won't shut me out, will you? Don't close your legs to me, I couldn't stand it.
Jackson

sometimes i wish my name was savannah. i don't know why i think that, it's just a substantial name. it takes time to say it. i don't much like my name. it's over too quickly. i say savannah and i can draw it out like they do down south, say it to a silent count.

dori sounds dopey. i am a dope. i don't know anything.

i don't think i am a serious person. i sit here alone and think too much. i worry, jackson. we don't have a future. i don't know what i am doing. i keep trying things out but nothing feels right. i feel good when i am in your arms but when you leave i seem to lose my identity. i feel like a shade, passing back and forth between lives, daylight to dark.

i talk to savannah about it all the time. she's the one you want.

i know this because she's the one i want.

I want Dori. Savannah sounds like trouble. I can't even spell it, I had to keep looking at your letter to remember was it two v's or two n's? Leave that name alone! Please. It can only bring trouble. It makes me jittery to say it. It doesn't suit you. Dori is a beautiful name like Doric which is a type of Greek column, classic. Like you. That other name sounds like a prostitute or some misguided actress that used to be called Mabel. Listen, Dori, I gotta paint this week, I'm way behind and there's a gallery pressuring. I can't work under so much strain. Last night I dropped ash in the picture and Rollo said to just leave it. He told me the coughing was from too many cigarettes. He laughed that way he does with his accent. He thinks you're very beautiful, by the way. He likes your breasts. I said what is it about a woman's breasts and Rollo said they sustain life. Huh! He always has a good answer. He talked about us doing a threesome. Uh-uh, I told him. Not with Dori. Anyway I left the ash stuck in the wet paint. You can't believe the shit that's landed in some of my pictures. This Sav— whatever the fuck name it is— just leave it alone please, Dori. You're making spider webs in my head again. I want out of the web. I should call this picture I'm doing *Out of the Web*. Maybe it will lead me out, what do you think? Meantime why don't you ask your girlfriend Patti to spend a few days in the cabin? It's been warmer during the day and you could go out rowing. Did you notice the row boat lying in the tall grass? Maybe you haven't but the oars are probably underneath. I thought it looked OK. Check it for cracks before you take it out. I don't need you drowning on me. If you drowned I'd go so far down. They could drag the bay for a year and they'd never recover my body. Do you get what I'm saying? Any of it? And not 'cause your dumb, I wouldn't spend my time with a dumb girl. I know I can't say love but this is just as good. You're it for me. In all of it— paint, brushes, my hands— JESUS! I'm exhausted. Dori call Patti, OK?

Were you good this week? Did you miss me? Did Patti come to see you? I'm taking you to New York. I'm bringing over the Ford this week and you can drive it into Southampton and buy some new dresses. I'll give you extra money. Will that make you happy? I hope you have put that Savannah business to rest. I need you Dori and can't go this long again.

Forever.
Jackson

Please don't criticize Savannah. You can write her name S, that's how I do it. Didn't you have an imaginary friend when you were little, Jackson? Someone to talk to?
Savannah is my oldest friend. In school I learned about friendship from a teacher once, how someone said "a true friend is like another you."

Savannah knows me better than Patti. Patti is OK, but she talks too much. She wants to know everything about us. I don't like to talk about us, Jackson. Not to Patti or Rusty or Rollo or any of your friends.

Please don't talk to your friends about our love. When we make love. You know, that's creepy. That makes me sick to my stomach. I only want to love you. I don't have room in my life for anything else right now.

But I'm frightened, Jackson. How can you be my mother and father and lover and friend? And do your paintings too?

I look out the window at the bay and talk to Savannah. Sometimes I sing to her. I like my voice. It cheers me sometimes. I like to listen to my singing better than my talking. I may give up on talking, like the monks. People do not know when to stop. The world is better silent.
Sometimes I think Pascal was right, that the troubles of the world would be less if we would just stay in our rooms, and not leave. Going out is trouble. Talk is trouble.

I don't want Patti, I want you. When will you come to me? I am lonesome. I don't want to go out in the boat without you. I don't want to leave the room. I sleep a lot. I sleep more than I should, Jackson. I am soft and lazy without you. And getting older, day by dreary day. It is cold and drafty in the cabin.

Come to me. D

I don't like this Savannah business one iota Dori. Not one
iota. Don't go off in that zone, it ain't a good place to be.
Trust me on that. She doesn't exist. Not in your mind or
anywhere. Make her (it) go away. It's like a bad ghost that
will start to eat away your skin then your organs. I know that
kind of ghost because sometimes when I paint it comes
visiting. All of a sudden I feel taken over, like something else
has a grip on me and I have to go along whether I want it or
not. But when I'm done painting, it goes away. I'm worried
for you Dori. Let me buy you a whole pile of dresses for
New York. Do you want me to drive you to Southampton to
get them? We could make a day of it. I'll do that for you,
Dori, anything for you. I'm crazy busy but I will make the
time. What do you say?
Who is Pascal?

Yours,
Jackson

It's no good without you. I don't want dresses I want you.
At night I am lonely and I touch myself. I cannot sleep and I
get bored and try to think where you are or what are you
doing? And it makes me upset and then I cry. I am not
getting older, I was wrong. I am getting younger, Jackson, I
am getting small and invisible and I hear the voices again, the
ones I heard when I was little. They talk to me all night till I
have to cover my head with the pillow. They don't like me.
Even Savannah won't talk to me. I am hungry and cold and
lonely.

No matter what is pressing I'm coming on Friday. I'm coming to see you and hold you and fuck you and kiss you and sleep with you after. I'm staying the whole night. Will that help ease your worries? What do you mean by saying you're hungry? I stocked the refrigerator with enough food to last a month! Just light the stove and cook some soup, that's easy. Make a sandwich of that ham shank. Light the fireplace and sleep on the couch, bring a pillow and blanket and sleep on the couch all night in front of the fire. That will warm you till Friday. Christ I'm getting worried about you. Don't run away again, Dori, please. For me. For Jackson. When you get scared and lonely just say I'm waiting for Jackson and he'll be here Friday. Then Saturday he's taking me to Southampton to buy a lot of new dresses. Then he's taking me to New York with him because I mean so much to him.

Write all that down Dori so you don't forget. Friday is very soon.

Forever and ever,

Jackson

Friday, then. Good Friday. Hurry.

Silly Jackson. I can't cook! I thought you knew that. It's
hysterical. I could burn water, it's that bad. I made some
macaroni and cheese and dropped the bowl on my foot.
Now I have a big toe that droops. I am hopeless in every
domestic task, mother insists. I was not meant to cook or
clean, Jackson, they raised me to just look at me, like a picture
on the wall. Now look at me. Dirty and starving in a dusty
old cabin.

You'll have to feed and clothe me, bathe me, take me—
I am here, waiting.

dori

I love a new dress. I like the feel of the fabric against my cool skin. I want to dress up for you, and take your arm. I want to go to the city, yes yes yes. To the Village, Jackson, take me to the dark basements to be with people who won't judge me and to hear the music till I cry.

Not another word about Savannah. You just don't understand. It's no use explaining to you, Jackson, you are hopeless. You are all about being new, your art makes all things new, but you are hopelessly old fashioned! Look at the car you drive! I think you are a man out of time. You amuse Savannah, but I adore you.

Don't delay,

dori

Yes, the city, soon! You sound so much better my Dori.

Your body is everywhere. I walk through the grass to my studio the flowering cherry is just starting to form buds and I see your little cunt hanging from a branch. When I separate you to make love I think how could Dori push out a baby, she's so small there. Dori you were a picture in those dresses. And it did make you happy! You twirled for me! The filmy turquoise one with the wide skirt lifted like air under wings— little sea bird. But why do I keep seeing death in the color of every drop of paint?

Jackson, don't speak of death! It's bad luck, mother says. Everyone knows that.

I love my dresses. I felt new, being with you. I loved the dances we danced, loved every minute. I loved the sound of the band, like a giant wall of sound I kept knocking into. I love being in the city so much, I want to go back, please Jackson. Why can't we live there? I know, I know, but don't talk logic to me, it's boring. Tell me why we can't continue doing what we just did when we both love it so much? I don't understand when you say no to me, when your heart tells you different.

Don't speak of babies either, you know how I feel. Babies cannot have babies.

You made me. Do you like what you made? I am your most current creation. One that talks back to you!

dori

But, Dori, did you like my pictures? Just a little?

My picture *Birds of Paradise* is you and me Dori. It's the one having the white swirls toward the center, you pointed and said it reminded you of your scarf with the swirls. Where is that scarf? I hope you didn't lose it.

Here are some of my favorite things:

oranges
the ocean
calico kittens
dogs named trouble
steamships— i would love to take a cruise across the north
atlantic with you!
the movies
the way you frown at me sometimes, when you're displeased
with me— your furrows!
the color blue. also purple. sometimes yellow.
my feet and hands— i like the extreme parts of me. the parts
closer to the center tend to trouble me
daisies
the wind

it was the wind that got the scarf, jackson. i am so sorry.
i am a careless girl.

d

Waking up without you next to me is bad, very bad. I kicked a hole in the closet door. I got out of bed and next thing my foot was through the door. I'm hobbling around like a Peg-leg-Pete, it's all swelled up. Now we match, Dori, you with your droopy toe and me with my fat foot. Do you know how proud I am to have you for my girl? You don't know what a knock-out you are. When we walked in the pub the other night with you in that tomato-red dress every jaw in the place dropped. No man could take his eyes off you. I couldn't stop touching your arms. How did you get born with arms so long and creamy? I wanted to fuck you right there on the table. Rollo can't stop talking about you. Watch out for him, Dori, he can sneak up on a woman. He's my friend and a damn fine painter but competitive. It's like he tabs up— a win for Jackson, a win for Rollo. He don't say it but it's there just the same. So watch out for him. You need to eat more Dori. I bought you that nice steak and you hardly ate two bites. You did OK with the cocktails though. Don't let Rollo kiss you on the lips again. When he goes for your lips, turn your head to the side so he gets your cheek. I'm the only man who gets those lips. And your breasts and your cunt. I'm possessive of what's mine.
Forever.
Jackson

Next time I see you (very soon) I want you to tell me you
love me. Just hold me tight and say I love you Jackson.
Make sure you say my name so I'll be sure it's me you love.

I'm coming to the cabin on Saturday, Dori. I'm bringing you
a present. No more dresses, you'll have to wonder.

Oh Jackson, Rollo is harmless. You get so jealous! You turned as red as my dress when he tried to kiss me. I like to kiss. I like the way it feels when your tongue explores inside my mouth, and touches my teeth and gums. And then when you pull away with soft, dry kisses.

I never kissed a boy until I was sixteen. It was at my sweet sixteen party with Johnny Strong. Isn't that a funny name? We played spin the bottle in the basement of my house, and I was laughing at his name, and then we wound up in the closet, kissing! He tried to force his tongue in my mouth and I was horrified! I can laugh now, but at the time it was no joking matter. I slugged him on the arm and told him to quit it. I was such a good girl. He calmed down after that and said he was sorry. Later, when the bottle pointed to us again, back into the closet we went, and he was slower that time, and even held me gently around the waist. He asked me to the prom but I wouldn't go. I didn't go with anyone. I had one of my little episodes that year, and I didn't feel up to it. Senior year he got some girl pregnant in Bridgehampton and that was that. I never saw him again. Pity, he was really a sweet boy, but not terribly bright. Poor dear.

I can see you shaking your head when you read this, your jaw tightening, getting all red in the face and jealous about some dumb high school basketball player! Oh, Jackson, I know you so well. You're going to rip this letter up and kick the wall and break your whole foot in two! You really are helpless without me, aren't you? I wonder if it will always be this way, if we mirror each other's emotions somehow? Am I your mirror, Jackson? Are we emotional equals, despite our ages? Or do you just want to fuck me?

I am preparing for your storm, now that I have your attention. There is a sailboat out on the bay and I watch it sail slowly away from me, taking all my thoughts with it. Goodbye, love. Goodbye, Jackson. as ever, dori

Dori do you really think I care about what boys you kissed? But I do care about you kissing Rollo— that is a definite no-no! Don't toy with me Dori, I don't like it. It will get me mad and then I'm no fun to be with. I want us to have fun and be close. You don't want to turn this into what I have with you-know-who. You definitely do not want that Dori. You'll run away forever, or maybe I'll be the first to run away. But one of us will go, it's a guarantee. Now look— I have a special gift for you, very special. It's like nothing you've ever seen before, it's rare. You are rare, too, my angel.
Jackson

See? I knew you'd get sore if I talked about kissing the boys!
Didn't I tell you?

Don't worry, silly. I am not going to kiss anyone today. My
lips are sealed, till I see you. I will only do practice kissing, on
the pillow, waiting for you to come to me! Lucky pillow,
lucky me. Jackson is coming to me.

What is it? What do you have for me? I love presents, but
you don't have to bring me anything, you know that. Just
your old ornery jealous self.

I told you not to speak of her. Ever. I mean it. She does not
exist to me. I don't want to hear another word.

Back to my pillow.

Don't be late, sweetie.

dori

Do you have a middle name? I cannot believe I never asked you this!

Mine is Jill.

Jackson & Jill.

Though I don't like the way that fairy tale ends.

I never knew what a crown was when I was a child. I kept asking mother, but I'm not sure she knew either.

Do you play golf, Jackson? There is so little I know about you, really. I cannot picture you as a golfer! You would get exasperated! My father taught me to play. He always wanted a boy, I think. We played at Shinnecock and Maidstone, and I am a good golfer. I liked to carry my own clubs but they made me use a caddie. For a while we had a putting green at the house, but mother insisted we use the space for another flower garden.

Am I boring you Jackson? Sometimes I prattle on. It is lonesome here. I may get the rowboat out, after all. I am feeling strong today.

Or maybe I'll play golf?

Jill

DORI. YOUR NAME IS DORI. KEEP THAT UNDER
YOUR PRETTY HEAD OF HAIR. No I don't play golf.
I'm a painter. A painter and your lover. That's the sum
total of my life.

What was your mother like, Jackson? I wonder about your parents, you never speak of them. Did they love you as my parents loved me? I was a breech baby. They nearly lost me, or so I was told. Father drove mother to the Southampton hospital in a freakish hailstorm! They were blown all over Rte. 27. Mother kept screaming at him to slow down!

She was a dancer in NY, she still has the long lean body of a dancer. She tried to make a ballet dancer out of me, but I rebelled. I preferred golf with father and that infuriated her! She's high strung (like someone you know!) and cannot accept anything but perfection. I was the perfect daughter, until she dropped me off the changing table when I was a baby and I hit my head. Mother never forgave herself for my "troubles," as she calls them.

Father would have made the perfect passenger on the Titanic, one of the men standing patiently aside, while they loaded women and children first into the lifeboats. I love my father so much, and I know that it kills him that I won't come home to him anymore. I admire men. But I think they are sad, really. Women bore me, honestly, with their pettiness and cat fighting, and the superficial talk. And then throwing each other over for a man! My mother had no patience for it, and she passed that on to me. Never fight over a man, she told me, and I haven't, ever. Sometimes, when Patti went on and on at the house in Montauk, who she saw, who was dating whom, I thought I would go stark raving mad. She got so mad at me when I clammed up about us.

Listen to me, now, going on like one of them. But when will I get to see my parents again, Jackson? This is such a small town. Word gets around. I am waiting for us to be found out. You seem unconcerned, but it's not your reputation on the line, is it? I'd have to move. Or you could marry me. Make a proper woman out of me.
Shall we give them something to talk about?

I was happy to see you out on the bay when I got there. I stood in the yard watching, you were further out than I expected you would go, and for a minute I got this little pull in my chest— like what if the rowboat is really no good and Dori is out there and starts to sink. I got scared. I haven't felt scared like that in maybe my whole life. Does that tell you what you mean to me? But then you saw me and waved and I waved and the fear went past. Climbing out of the boat you were so beautiful, slender but strong at the same time. And I thought I can die now and it won't matter because I've had Dori the way no man will ever know happiness. That picture of you pulling the boat to land then climbing out, flushed and alive and so young — it's permanently etched on my brain. I knew you'd like the gift. It's very rare to find these double bird eggs. I've heard them called Siamese twin eggs. I've only seen one other, a double blue robin egg. But this one is more special because of its pale shell and dark speckles. First I was going to drain it and make it into a necklace for you, pierce it with a thin piece of stiff metal so you could wear it as a choker. But that would mean taking off your heart locket. And somehow to drain it felt wrong. So I got to thinking now what am I gonna do about this double speckled egg that is so precious, for my precious Dori. Then I noticed the tiny wood box thrown in with my tools, and I picked it up and liked the way the top slid back to open. And I thought of you, Dori, how you are my little nest. So I put in some dry grass from right outside the door of my studio where you stood that first time you came here. Grass that was under your feet to make a nest for the double egg. I hope you will never lose this the way you let your scarf fly off.
Forever.
Jackson

Your letter came just as I was getting dressed to go out in the
boat on the bay. The postman peeked in and saw me
fastening my bra. Nothing else but a bra! I was mortified
and dropped the bra! I stood there frozen like a deer, then he
realized what had happened and covered his eyes and I leaped
behind the couch. It was comical. He sure got an eyeful!
Bare assed Dori! But not to worry, Jackson, he must be
nearly sixty or something, old enough to be my grandfather.
I just hope he doesn't talk.

Don't worry, I won't lose the egg. It is lovely. I keep it with
me by my pillow.

I wish I hadn't lost that old scarf you liked so well—

When are we going out dancing again? I miss the music,
Jackson. Promise me we'll go soon! I want to go tonight!

I found a new jar of cream to rub on my legs, moisturizer.
Mmmm. I smell so good for you, Jackson. My legs are
shaved and smooth and ready for you, to wrap around you
like a vise. I may not let go of you.

You are a lucky old SOB

Me

The postman is a lucky guy too. I think you did it on purpose. I think you knew he was out there and showed him your bare ass. I painted naked models for years, do you think him seeing you naked is going to upset me? Half the Art Student League ran around naked. Only the touching, Dori. Nobody touches you. Let them look all they like. Stand on the roof with your tits flying in the breeze if it makes you happy. But one guy touches you, it's over between you and me.

Dear Jackson Pollock,

I had to come down off the roof from sunning my titties to retrieve your letter from the postman, who was all a flutter.

Honestly, Jackson, you are exasperating at times. Do you honestly think I displayed my naked body in the window for an 80 year old man? That I live to do that?

And those artist models that you mention in your letter— did YOU touch any of them? Did you ever hear me asking any questions. As if I care.

Oh, don't let's fuss over any of this, Jackson. None of it matters.

What matters is that the old man keeps his trap shut, and that everyone else that has seen us together does the same thing. It's a lot to ask. I don't want ANYONE telling HER anything. Do you understand? I want us to remain invisible to the outside world. That's why it hurts me so much that you would think I displayed myself in the raw for some silly old householder from Islip, or wherever he is from.

Sometimes it feels like I'm the adult in this relationship.

My heart is yours. Take care of it, Jackson.

xox

dori

OK. OK. I'm sorry. But one minute you're crying in the pillow the next you're giving the postman a hard on. Dori I apologize. But you make my head spin at times. I don't care who knows about us. I want everyone to know, that's how proud of you I am. In fact I would say a lot of people know about us. We go places and people see us together. I'm not going to hide you in a cave my Dori. Don't let it trouble you. You are my true bride.
Always,
Jackson

Jackson, I repeat: What you don't know about women is a lot.

You call me your bride— then let's get married, properly, in a church. I want a big church wedding, with all our friends and half the art world, the part that won't make us sick to our stomachs. Say you will, Jackson. Propose to me. Make me yours.

This is the first time I remember that you actually apologized to me. At least in a letter. That is something. You know what I think? I think that art is your true wife, and the rest of us are just mistresses. I am no one's mistress, Jackson. I want you to hear me on this. A mistress is always in second place. Or third or fourth. I wasn't raised to take second place.

So I <u>do</u> care what people think. If we are going to be seen in public then I need to know what I am going AS when I go out with you. Am I going as your bride? Am I going as your fiancé? Until you decide, then DO NOT tell anyone else about us, and the ones who already know had better keep their mouths shut. Or they'll have me to answer to.

I am not some mistress you can throw aside when you get tired or bored. I am a person with feelings and hopes and dreams, just like everyone else. I need to know what I am DOING with my life, baby, can't you see? Am I going to stay in some stupid cabin the rest of my life waiting for you to make time for me?

It is such a lovely spring day. I am going out now. I hate it when I have to write letters like this to you. I don't want to write any more letters. I'm done with letters. Give me a ring, Jackson. On my finger. Leave her, or send her packing. Install me at your place. I will always be your muse, you told me that. What are you going to do without me? Your dori

Dori I know I have apologized to you before. Half my life is a fucking apology. I do things wrong. I don't mean to but it comes out half assed and stupid even when I try not to. If you think I stink now you should've seen me when the drinking was really bad. My brother's wife kicked my ass out of their apartment so many times. She said I was a bad influence on him. I wouldn't have stood a chance with you during those times. You would've said who is this bum Jackson Pollock and you would have high-tailed it the hell out. Now look Dori. I've got pressure from my sponsor for that show coming up in the city and that gallery in Paris that's hanging some pictures. I gotta paint all the time to meet my deadlines. You think I enjoy not seeing you every day? I want to go out in the boat with you then come back to shore and jump you in the grass. I want to suck the salt out of you. So that you'll be sweet to me again.
Forever.
Jackson

That's the B answer, Jackson. Or maybe the D or F answer.

Actually it is no answer at all, as you ignored my questions.

Return to Sender.

What exactly do you mean by this Dori?
I can't install a phone line in a cabin that don't belong to me.
Or do you suppose I can?
You think the world revolves around us?
We're just shadows.

Dori you don't understand. It's because of your age and that you never had to scratch your way up. I've had a life of vicious extremes. Did you never wonder why I skipped the army? The army skipped me, claimed I was too unstable to be a soldier. I felt a fair amount of shame over it. Now I want to tell you something else. Those dresses I bought you for New York, the floaty turquoise one and the hot tamale red in particular. You didn't want them at first, you said they weren't your colors. But I pushed you, Dori, remember? And you saw yourself in the shop mirror and the way they lit up your skin and hair and eyes. Those colors brought a turning point for me. Turquoise and red and cream yellow in my picture *Stenographic Figure*. Things started to change for me then. It got hung in the new gallery Art of this Century. It turned a corner for me, Dori. Got me out of the filth, the stench dog existence. An evil that I was pulling up and out of. So I wanted to see you in those colors. Not to paint you into that picture but to remind myself.
Forever.
Jackson

Jackson,

The bay is calm today. It's a lovely spring morning, Mayday. When I was a little girl we played games on Mayday. I ran and ran around the schoolyard with the boys chasing me.

I want to go out on the water today. From my chair outside I can see the gulls circle and land. I saw an eagle yesterday! Since I have been here I have seen Osprey and Ruddy Duck, Tree Swallows, Catbird, Thrasher, and Mourning Dove. And a Black Guillemot with white winter plumage.

Oh Jackson, you still don't understand, do you? I have had so much time to think out here, by myself in my chair, or lying awake at night in my bed. I stare at the cabin walls and try to see the future. I have decided that you are most alive in your art. And when you are making love to me. And these two things are the same to you.

I didn't ask for this to happen, it just did. You just showed up with your pain like a little green dot in the middle of your head that called to me. We recognized each other. How could I not love you?

Yes, you pushed me, and opened me up. You saved me, Jackson. They say that small towns breed small minds, well maybe that is true. I don't know. But I think that I didn't see the colors in the world until I met you, it was all shades of gray like the Atlantic in the winter.
But it is almost June and we have no plan. Maybe we don't need a plan. Maybe we can go on this way, a day at a time. I don't know.

I want an education, Jackson. I want to go back to school. I was a fool to get kicked out. I was with the wrong crowd, and I was the skinniest, so they made me climb through the window and steal those tests and I didn't know how to stand up to them. They thought I was stuck up because I held myself apart, and they tested me, and I gave in. Pretty girls suffer too, Jackson, though it's hard to feel pity. But I would trade my looks, hack my hair off, dress in a burlap bag, and grow out every hair on my legs to be a serious person. I wrote that silly letter to make light of it but I was a fool and now I have paid.

But it brought me you. And now look at you, poor dear. You don't know what to do with me. The women in your life bring you nothing but trouble!

I'll not nag you, Jackson. I will never do that again. You have enough of that in your life. You want what you want. I'm just saying that I want things, too, though I often don't know what they are until I lose them. I know I am young and don't understand so many things, but maybe we are just trying to find a place where we can stay the longest without lying to each other.

It's like an open air cathedral here. Even my sighs feel like prayers. I love being with you. I love you. Maybe the muse isn't supposed to say that, it seems too direct, but I do, Jackson.

You always liked when I used your name. Jackson, Jackson, Jackson, it's Mayday and I love you, and that's a pity, isn't it? It's only when you open your heart that you can really get hurt. So that's what I have learned living out here. It isn't much God knows, but I am a slow learner. your dori

Dori, Dori, beautiful Dori. My sea bird. Right now my brain feels very tired. I'm painting every minute I'm awake to keep up with their fucking schedule. They treat me like a clock. Wind Pollock, let him wind down, wind him back up. Dori I'll figure out something for us, I don't want you worrying. I think of you worrying and I see you like those women hanging wash on the line, once so pretty but now strained. You keep worrying your looks will burn out early. I know it's been a while and god knows it's killing me too. I need your body under me, on top, twisted around me like a vine you can't snap off. You are what's there always, everywhere, in my eyes— others must see it too. I wish I could write more but it's back outside to work. This is my curse. We all get one.

I like that you're watching the birds, they know things we don't.

j,

i left.

i am in montauk now again. it feels right to be here. I hope you'll understand—

meet me out on old montauk highway by the big dune, you know the one.

at dusk. come before dark.

if you're not there i will walk toward the sea. the birds will know where i am.

come, jackson.

d

Pollock held the car to fifty. It was an old model and it was all he could do to keep it to the road. As he drove east from the city his optimism vanished. The color of the day was drained from the sky. He picked up Route 27.

The land began to change. It was late spring. The faint smell of the sea was in the air. He passed the burnt out foundation of an ancient house set back from the road. Here and there along the road isolated frame houses held nothing of what he wanted. It was almost night when he passed through Amagansett. He turned off on Old Montauk Highway.

She was waiting by the dune.

The wind off the ocean blew her pale hair back into her face each time she pushed it away with her hand. She was a tall drink of a girl. She swayed in the wind, her arms wrapped around her chest, her slender frame knocked backward and pushed toward the angry Atlantic.

Pollock waved at her and walked faster. She ran to him and they embraced, then pulled away to look at each other. She was as tall as he, and they stood there a while with their foreheads tapping together, a perfect fit.

Fog was moving up the coast and Pollock felt her moist cheeks against his and saw the way her mouth parted for his tongue and understood that he was a lucky man, despite his recent troubles. It pained him to hold those thoughts together.

He knew if he could keep from speaking he could present himself to this moment more completely, that it was words that ruin things in the end. Words speeded every ending and Pollock meant to stay ahead of this one if he could. He doubted his ability to do anything but look at her and go on looking at her and then paint her from memory.

He understood that a girl like this could not be made to keep still. Or do anything else she didn't want to.

He drew her into a long kiss and felt something stern and gray pass between them in the fog, a shade of feeling that seemed to go all the way through him till the sea and the crying birds and the salt air were one and the salt of his tears mixed with hers. He knew then that he would have to speak. But it was Dori who spoke first.

"She knows."

He nodded.

"You told her?"

"She always knew."

The girl considered this. "Well then, don't say anything more."

She wanted to pull away but he held her firm by the waist.

"Dori."

"Yes?"

He let go of her then and looked down at the sand. A gust of wind swept over the dune blowing pieces of grit into his face, and he shielded his eyes from the fury of it. His hands hurt from painting in the cold studio and he cursed his luck and picked up a stone. It fit snugly in his palm and the coldness of it made him forget his throbbing hands. He threw it skipping into the waves and they watched as it sank. A fishing boat was moving in the middle distance, its lights haloed in the fog.

Pollock turned back to her. She studied him in the dying light. It occurred to him that he could share with her the thoughts he'd pieced together in the car, lay them out in sequence, with the earliest, tidiest first, just lay them down.

He flexed his jaw, returning her gaze. She moved her hand from his leg. Then he licked his lips and tried to smile. He opened his mouth to speak.

But he couldn't remember.

ABOUT THE AUTHORS

Susan Tepper is the author of *Deer & Other Stories* and the poetry collection *Blue Edge*. Over one hundred of her stories, poems, essays and interviews have been published in journals and anthologies worldwide. Prior to taking up the writing life, Tepper was an actor, singer, flight attendant, marketing manager, television producer, interior decorator, rescue worker and a few other things. *Where You Can Find It,* her newly completed novel, is up for grabs. If she were around during Jackson Pollock's time, she believes she would have been one of his girlfriends.

Gary Percesepe is Associate Editor at the *Mississippi Review* and serves on the Board of Advisors at *Fictionaut*. His short stories, poems, essays, book reviews, interviews, literary and film criticism, and articles in philosophy and religion have been published in *Mississippi Review, Salon, Antioch Review, Westchester Review, Schuylkill Valley Journal, Stymie Magazine, New Ohio Review, Pank, Luna Park, Corium, Istanbul Literary Review, elimae, Wigleaf, Metazen,* and other places. A former philosophy professor, he is the author of four books in philosophy, including *Future(s) of Philosophy: The Marginal Thinking of Jacques Derrida.* He just completed a novel called *Leaving Telluride.*